MOUSEBOUND

a farcical tale of rodent rebellion

WRITTEN BY

LESLIE ANN GEORGE

ILLUSTRATED BY

MELISSA O'GRADY

First Edition: August 2018

Book Designer: K.R. Conway, CapeCodScribe.com
Illustrator: Melissa O'Grady

Library of Congress Cataloging-in-Publication Data
George, Leslie Ann
Mousebound/ by Leslie Ann George – First Edition.
    Pages: 46
    Summary: Two mice have the run of the house until a big tabby cat moves in and challenges their way of life, triggering the mice to fight dirty.

PO Box 300
West Barnstable, MA 02668
ISBN: 978-1-7325596-0-8
Published in the United States of America

For Dad

One day, two mice named Woody and Jacob moved into a small single-story house on a quiet tree-lined street. They'd tried other homes in the neighborhood, big ones with large families and pets, where food was plentiful. But gathering it was riskier. This house, however, was home to only one older woman who was out for most of the day.

While she was gone, Woody and Jacob had the run of the place. They would scurry around the floor eating the crumbs she dropped during breakfast. Then they'd climb on the counter to lick the dirty dishes and drink from the water that pooled in the sink.

The mice spent hours playing tag and hide-and-seek on the fluffy white carpet that covered the living room. When they got tired, they'd stretch out on the velvety sofa cushions to take a nap. But they were always careful to retreat to their hiding space, which was a small gap in the wall behind a baseboard, before the woman returned home. Woody and Jacob had never been happier.

They couldn't believe their good fortune and before long they became very comfortable with their routine - in fact a little too comfortable.

It just so happened that on one afternoon they were still groggy from all the eating and playing, and were fast asleep on the furniture when the woman returned. When she saw the mice, she shrieked, startling them so severely that they froze and didn't know which way to run. She grabbed a broom from the hall closet and rushed toward them.

"EEEEEEK! Get out, you rats! Get out of my house!"

She was much faster than she looked. The mice leapt off the couch and darted across the floor in different directions. The woman swatted furiously at their little grey bodies as they fled, yelling at them the whole time. The broom's corn bristles brushed the tip of Woody's tail just before he ducked into the hole behind Jacob.

Both mice remained hidden for the rest of the day and vowed to be more careful in the future. Immediately following the encounter, however, they noticed that the woman was extra careful to clean up before she left. As a result, there were no crumbs on the floor and no plates in the sink. Woody and Jacob realized that they'd have to change their strategy if they wanted to eat.

They scaled the counter and sniffed their way over to the breadbox. Together they used their strength to push open the roll-top door. Once inside, they dragged out a loaf of bread, chewed through the bag, and shared a slice on the counter.

After they were full, it occurred to them that hunting for food might start to get harder, so they brought a few extra slices to store in the wall for later. The mice spent the whole day checking the cabinets for anything else that looked good, like crackers, cereal, and nuts, and hoarded some of those items as well.

When the woman returned home and saw the open cabinets, nibbled bread, and torn pieces of bag on the counter, she was furious. "What is this?" she huffed. "What have you little buggers been into?"

She raced around the kitchen like a tornado, her feet shaking the floor as Woody and Jacob watched wide-eyed from the safety of their den behind the baseboards. "This is the last straw!" she hollered, tossing the chewed boxes of cereal and crackers into the garbage. "I'll take care of you one way or another!"

That night she was so upset she couldn't sleep. As she lay awake in bed, she remembered the alley cat she passed each day on her way to the bus stop. He was often sitting on the sidewalk, staring into the trees as he hunted for birds, but she never paid him much mind.

Because he looked like a big bear, everyone called him Teddy. He was a strong cat, rugged and orange with a tattered ear and matted fur. She wondered if he might appreciate the luxuries that accompanied a life indoors.

The next morning the woman woke early and left the house on a mission, returning shortly thereafter with her arms full of supplies. By the mouse hole she set up a big box and filled it with sand. Near the sofa she tossed a fleece-lined pad and a carpeted post with a feathery toy attached to the top. Afterwards she went to the kitchen and put down two bowls that she filled with crunchy morsels and water.

Woody and Jacob watched her attentively but were curious when she left again. They wondered if she'd changed her mind about them and decided to make amends by giving them a sandbox, a little playground, and their own private buffet. Unfortunately, their hopes were thwarted when she returned with a big orange cat in her arms. She plopped him down in the middle of the living room. "Okay, Teddy, I'm going to make you a deal. You'll never have to spend another day hungry on that cold, dirty street as long as you keep those pesky mice out of this house!"

The cat just looked at her lazily, tipping his head up to sniff the air. He was delighted by how good it smelled, like fresh flowers and lemon-scented wood polish. He stretched out his claws and kneaded the carpet. It felt so soft on his calloused, street-hardened paws.

He walked over to the big couch and jumped on it. The only time he'd ever seen furniture was when someone in the neighborhood set an old, broken piece out on the curb for the trash men to cart away. He rubbed his face against the cushions, claiming them for his own, and began to purr.

For the next few weeks, the woman and the cat were very pleased with their new arrangement. Since the cat didn't have to spend hours a day hunting for his food, he had ample time to lie around and wash. Before long his coat was silky and clean, he was never cold, and he always had plenty to eat.

The woman was additionally satisfied because there were no signs of mice. At night the pair would hunker down in the bed, purring and snoring, while the cat kept one ear open at all times for the pitter-patter of tiny rodent feet.

Meanwhile, the mice were growing very frustrated. A few times Woody or Jacob would try to sneak into the kitchen while the other kept watch, but before they got very far the cat would sense movement and spring to action, forcing them to retreat. He was patient and could wait for hours crouching in front of their hole.

One afternoon the mice were lying on their backs, listening to their stomachs growl. "If we don't do something soon, we're going to starve to death," said Jacob. "We need to come up with a plan."

"Well," said Woody, "Remember how mad that lady got when she saw what a mess we made of her kitchen. Maybe if she thinks the cat is messy she'll want to get rid of him, too!"

"That's a great idea, but how do we do that?"

The two mice thought for a minute. "I have an idea!" said Jacob, peeking out of the hole. The cat was asleep on the sofa, warming his fur from a sunbeam that streamed through the window. "Shh," he said to Woody, putting a finger over his lips, before tiptoeing out.

Jacob moved slowly, keeping his back close to the baseboard as he carefully crept toward the litter box. He made another check of the cat before grabbing the rim of the box with his tiny paws and heaving himself over the side.

A small poof of dust rose up as he landed. Jacob crouched down to make sure the cat hadn't heard. When he realized it was safe, he dug around until he found a single sand-covered turd. He picked it up and launched it over the side. He watched with anticipation as it soared through the air, bounced on the carpet, and then rolled even further into the middle of the room. Satisfied, Jacob quickly sprinted back inside the wall.

"That was great!" hollered Woody. "Good work!"

For the rest of the day the two mice waited anxiously. When they finally heard the jingle of keys in the door, they rushed to the hole to watch.

"Hello, Teddy, I'm home," the woman said, taking her coat off.

The cat yawned, stretched, and climbed down from the couch to greet her. He meowed cheerfully, slinking in and out of her legs while she patted his head.

"How is my good hunter?" she asked, proudly ushering him into the kitchen to set out his dinner.

Only after he'd stuck his big head in the bowl, did she venture off to the bedroom to change. That's when she saw it. How could she not? In the middle of the clean, white carpet lay a single turd, completely decamped from the box.

"What is this?" she shrieked.

Teddy kept eating. Surely the woman wasn't talking to him, he thought. He was doing a great job holding up his end of the bargain. He crouched deeper onto his haunches to get more comfortable while he munched. Suddenly, he felt her hands pluck him up from his armpits. He was whisked away from his bowl and deposited onto the living room floor.

"Did you do this?" she asked, pointing at the lone turd.
The cat was just as surprised to see it as she was. He even walked over to sniff it suspiciously for confirmation that it was indeed his. At a loss for an explanation, he wrinkled up his nose and walked away to groom himself.

"Listen here, Teddy," scolded the woman. "I'm going to give you the benefit of the doubt and assume this was a freak accident, but if I see anymore messes, you're out of here! Do you understand me?"

Woody and Jacob were giggling so hard they could barely contain themselves. They spent the rest of the evening acting out the scene, laughing just as hard each time.

That night, the cat was leery so he stayed awake. He perched on his bed beside the sofa to keep an eye on the box. The mice, however, knew better than to risk coming out. The next morning the woman was pleased to see that no further accidents had occurred. She patted Teddy on the head and left for the day.

By mid-morning, Teddy kept yawning. He was exhausted from staying up all night. He tried to fight the urge to take a short nap, but the sunbeam that streamed through the window was beckoning him to bathe in its warmth. Just a few minutes, he thought, crawling onto the couch to let his fur have a momentary taste. His tired eyes squinted in the brightness as he began to purr. Within two minutes he fell fast asleep.

Woody and Jacob seized the opportunity and set out on their task. They crawled from the hole and slinked over to the box. Jacob climbed inside and passed the sand covered turds down to Woody, who rolled them like bowling balls as far as they would go.

They were almost finished when the cat woke suddenly and sprung from the couch. In a single leap, he was right in front of Jacob.

The petrified mouse stood in the middle of the box, holding the last of Teddy's droppings in his trembling little hands. Thinking fast, he threw it, hitting the cat in the middle of his pink triangle nose before catapulting himself over the side to flee.

Teddy was momentarily startled but quickly recovered and sprinted into action. He tracked Jacob's path through the sand, scattering granules everywhere with his big furry feet. Jacob leapt onto the coffee table, taunting the cat to follow. When Teddy jumped up, his weight rattled the table so much that it tipped over a lamp. He ignored the bang as it hit the floor and continued to swipe at the mouse with his paw. A single claw pierced the tip of Jacob's tail, halting him in his tracks.

Woody, seeing what was happening, squeaked loudly and jumped up and down to draw the cat's attention. Teddy redirected and took chase, scattering a pile of neatly stacked magazines in every direction.

Woody bolted into the kitchen, nimbly weaving in and out of the food bowls, but the cat was not as graceful. He plowed right through, spraying crunchies and water everywhere. In the wetness, the linoleum floor became slick and Teddy had a hard time holding his footing. His feet were pumping rapidly yet he was getting nowhere.

Meanwhile, Woody scaled a chair and climbed the dining table. He tipped over a salt shaker and rolled it to the edge where he gave it a final kick. It sailed down and hit the cat on his head before tumbling to the floor, scattering salt everywhere.

Teddy winced at the pain, but was determined to have something to show for all his trouble, so he shook himself off and launched up onto the table. From the floor, he couldn't see the cloth place mat. It slid out from under his feet as he landed. The more he scurried to pull himself up, the more the mat slipped. Eventually Teddy tumbled to the floor, landing on his feet with a big thud. The mat floated down behind him and draped limply over his head. That gave Woody enough time to get away and safely scurry to the hole. Inside, Jacob was waiting, relieved. Both mice flopped down inside the wall to catch their breath, but they could sense that Teddy was right outside.

The cat and the two mice held their positions for a long time until they heard keys in the door. Teddy instantly meowed and padded over to greet the woman. As she bent down to scratch his head, she saw the mess. Her jaw dropped in horror as she stepped deeper into her house. It looked like a cyclone had blown through.

"OH MY GOODNESS!" she shrieked. "What in heaven's name happened here? Did you do this?"

Teddy looked at her innocently, licking a paw and swiping it over his brow. After all, he'd only been doing what she'd asked.

"This is the final straw!" she said. "You're out of here!" She plucked the cat up by his scruff and deposited him on the front stoop. A gust of air rippled Teddy's fur as she slammed the door shut behind him.

Teddy sat on the stoop a moment, waiting to see if the woman would change her mind. When she didn't, he shook himself off, trotted down the steps, and proudly ambled back to his old corner.

Meanwhile, Woody and Jacob were ecstatic as they watched the woman furiously running around cleaning. She straightened up the furniture, vacuumed and scrubbed the carpet, washed the kitchen floor, and tossed all of Teddy's things to the curb. When she was finally done, she filled two small bowls, one with bread pieces and the other with water. She set them by the baseboard in the living room. "Listen to me, you little buggers, are you in there? I want to make a deal."

Woody and Jacob poked their noses hesitantly out of the hole to look at her. Their round ears were cocked attentively.

She cringed at the sight of them, but shook off the disgust and continued. "If I leave you some morsels, will you promise to keep your filthy little critter fingers off of my food?"

They nodded.

"And will you stay off my furniture and promise not to scare the daylights out of me by running under my feet?"

They nodded again. It seemed like a fair deal under the circumstances.

"All right then. I'll make sure you always have snacks." She looked sternly at them. "But if you ever—and I mean ever—tell any of your little friends about this arrangement, I will call an exterminator in a heartbeat! Do you understand?"

Woody and Jacob squeaked agreeably and flicked their tails to display their appreciation. Satisfied, the woman shuffled off to bed.

The next morning, the big orange cat with the tattered ear was sitting motionless, staring up into a tree, when a man pushing a stroller walked by. "Oh, what do we have here?" he said. "What a nice, healthy-looking ginger kitty!"

The cat abandoned his bird hunting and meowed. He arched his back and weaved in and out of the man's legs. The man bent down to pat his head, and the toddler reached out to stroke him.

"We just moved into the neighborhood," he explained. "And there sure seem to be a lot of mice in our house. How'd you like to come live with us in exchange for some hunting? My wife is terrified of the little critters."

Teddy looked at him and purred.

"Okay, kitty, come on then." He pushed the carriage down the block with Teddy trotting along beside. On the way, they passed a brand new litter box, cat bed, and scratching post on the curb. "Oh my goodness, I can't believe our good luck!" he marveled, grabbing the items and balancing them around the stroller. He looked down at the cat and smiled. "I guess this was meant to be!"

The End

ACKNOWLEDGMENTS

I would like to thank my parents for their creativity, wit, and appreciation for the arts. Also for being so much fun to hang out with; otherwise I might have missed all of that wisdom.

Thanks to my oldest and dearest pals, for their unwavering support and encouragement, and for always providing useful, realistic advice. No matter how much time passes, we are always able to pick up right where we left off. I take great comfort in that.

Naturally, I could not have done any of this without Melissa O'Grady, whose delightful illustrations brought these characters to life. I am eternally grateful for her generosity of time and talent.

Thank you to K.R. Conway at Wicked Whale Publishing, whose expertise and astonishing time management skills made this process both fun and seemingly effortless.

Thanks to my writing group and all the beta readers who offered up their children and students as guinea pigs. I have appreciated the constructive suggestions.

And finally, to each and every one of the animals, big and small, wild and tame, that have passed in and out of my life: thank you for enriching my soul, keeping me grounded, and for teaching me to be a better human.

About the Author and Illustrator:

LESLIE ANN GEORGE is an American author, animal lover, and dreamer. She currently lives and writes on Cape Cod.

MELISSA O'GRADY is an illustrator, painter, and graphic novelist by night and a librarian by day. She has two cats who couldn't care less about mice and a little dog who lives for the chance to catch one. She lives in Cleveland, Ohio.

Find the author on Facebook and Twitter at
"Leslie Ann George"

42266990R00027

Made in the USA
Middletown, DE
15 April 2019